How To Handle Your Teacher

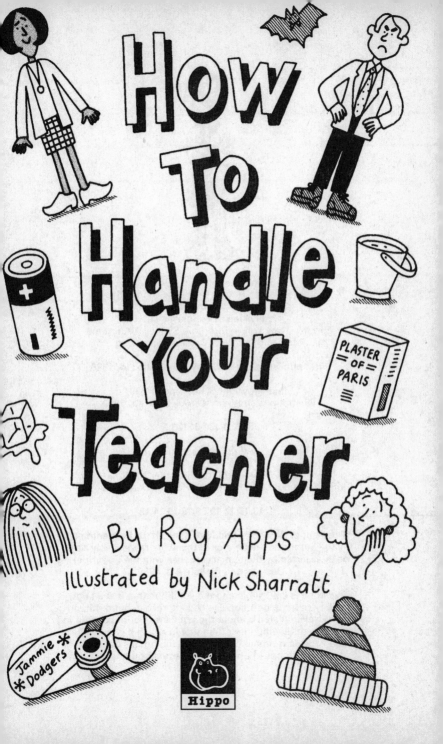

How To Handle Your Teacher

By Roy Apps

Illustrated by Nick Sharratt

Hippo

Scholastic Children's Books
Commonwealth House, 1-19 New Oxford Street,
London WC1A 1NU, UK
a division of Scholastic Ltd
Lndon ~ New York ~ Toronto ~ Sydney ~ Auckland
Mexico City ~ New Delhi ~ Hong Kong

First published in the UK by Scholastic Ltd, 1999

ISBN 0 439 01123 X

Typeset by TW Typesetting, Midsomer Norton, Avon
Printed and bound by Nørhaven Paperback A/S, Denmark

13 15 17 19 20 18 16 14 12

A Dreadful Warning!!!

Under no circumstances must you allow a TEACHER to get hold of this book. Some teachers can read, and if they read this book they will get to know your teacher-handling strategy. In other words, they will be forewarned. And as the proverb says, "Forewarned is forearmed." And if you thought this warning was dreadful, it's nothing compared to a four-armed teacher:

Told you.

There are two things you can do to make sure your teacher doesn't read this book...

1 You can put it somewhere your teacher will never find it – like in a block of reinforced concrete, 20 metres under the school playing field. The trouble with this solution is that you'll need a JCB, a pneumatic drill and a team of navvies every time you want to read a bit of it.

2 You can disguise the cover so that no teacher would ever dare to pick it up – let alone read it. A kind of undercover overcover. A suitable undercover overcover disguise can be found opposite...

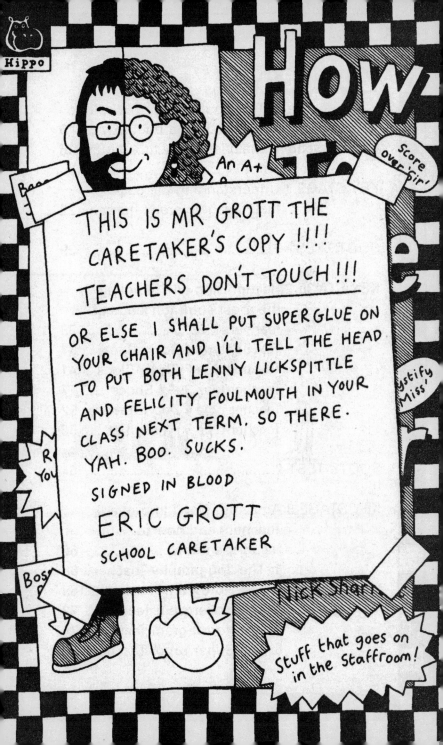

Contents

IT ALL STARTED LIKE THIS...

It was a wonderfully balmy* summer's evening. I'd just spent a couple of hours surfing the net.

And to tell you the truth, I'd finally decided that trying to fish from a surfboard was a bad idea.

I went home, logged on and checked my computer mailbox for e-mails. There weren't any.

ZILCH!

*Dear Mr Writer, Are you sure you don't mean *barmy* evening? Kind regards, The Publisher.

So I checked my other mailbox for fe-mails, instead...

A young girl jumped out. She had a mountain bike in one hand and a large white envelope in the other.

"This is for you," she said.

"Thanks very much," I replied. "I've always wanted a mountain bike."

"Not the mountain bike!" the girl retorted. "The envelope. Read it, pea brain."

2 THAT BLOAK WOT RITES THEM
HOW TERRANDLE BOOX

I read.

The girl leapt on to her saddle and pedalled off. I felt very hurt. This was because I was still holding on to the saddle at the time.

I went back inside, put my feet up on the sofa and tore open the envelope.

Inside there was a letter. In fact, there were lots of letters. And they were all written down on a page of paper like this:

Ghastley Junior School

Dear Bloak Wot Rites Them How Terrandle Boox,

You av dun a nace jobb lerning Kidz ow terrandle thair mums, dads, grans, bruvversansisters and stuff. But, ime tellin yer mate, mums, dads, grans and bruvversansisters and stuff are ded eezy terrandle Kompaired to the peepole hoo make my ole heggistents sutch a Flippin misserie. I meen off corse, the curse an the bane off my lyfe, TEECHERS! Theyr kompleetly an nutterly outer Kontrolle! Pleez, pleez, halp a por ole man hoosat is witzend and rite a boock lerning ev ree wun ow terrandle blooming teechers.

Yorse in Seerly
I. Mincharge (Headmaster)

I was amazed! To think that a Headmaster could write a letter like that! I mean, what is a Headmaster for, if it isn't for keeping teachers under control? Goodness, some of my best friends were Head teachers, not to mention some of my best fiends.

There was nothing else for it. I would have to do something I never managed to do in all my 13 years at school; I would have to do what the Headmaster told me. I would have to sit down and write a book lerning ev ree wun ow terrandle blooming teechers.

BACK TO SCHOOL

To be honest, I was looking forward to writing a book called *How to Handle Your Teacher*. I thought it would be a piece of cake.* All I had to do was to refresh my memory of my days at school. Although it was many years since I had left my school, I knew exactly where I had left it – right on the corner of Canal Street:

The first person I saw was my old teacher Mr Meesley-Grewell. He hadn't changed much, except that he wasn't so much my old teacher Mr Meesley-Grewell, more like my ancient teacher, Mr Meesley-Grewell.

*I was of course, wrong. I found this out after I'd finished writing the book and then tried eating it one Sunday teatime. Yes, there was no doubt about it, *How To Handle Your Teacher* most definitely was not a piece of cake.

crunch!

Our conversation went something like this, or rather, it went precisely like this:

ME: (CHEERILY) Hello, Mr Meesley-Grewell!

MR M-G: (ANGRY) Ah, Ponsonby, have you finished it yet?

ME: Finished what, Mr Meesley-Grewell?

MR M-G: Your project on "Why I Think Climbing Chimneys Is An Incredibly Useful Job For a Boy To Do".

ME: (MUTTERING) Er ... my quill ran out of ink, sir.

MR M-G: I want the truth, lad!

ME: (GOING RED AS A BEETROOT) I haven't done it, Mr Meesley-Grewell.

MR M-G: (FUMING) Haven't done it, eh? 35 years you've had to finish that piece of work!

ME: (SHAKING FROM HEAD TO FOOT) Yes, Mr Meesley-Grewell, sir. I know Mr Meesley-Grewell, sir.

MR M-G: (DEAD ANGRY) You can stay in at play time and finish it then!

I ran away from that school just as fast as my legs would carry me. I fell over at the school gate and hurt my ankle, so then I had to run away just as fast as I could carry my legs.

My terrifying experience with Mr Meesley-Grewell had got me thinking: 35 years ago I'd left school and I'd not seen or heard from Mr Meesley-Grewell until that dreadful moment when I had gone back to Canal Street. Where had he been all those years? Where had all the other teachers been all those years? Where did teachers go when they weren't at school? Where did teachers come from? Or to put it another way – from come teachers did where?

I had to find out. What I would do would be to follow Mr Meesley-Grewell home from school. Given what had happened to me when he had last seen me, I thought I'd better go under cover.

So next day at half past three, I stood out-side Canal Street Primary School. And true to my word, I was under cover. Under my Paddington Bear duvet cover to be precise.

I followed Mr Meesley-Grewell along the street. Soon he turned down another street, then he turned into a large wrought iron gate.

Amazing! I had no idea he was such a talented magician.

Mr Meesley-Grewell went up the path to a large house. The door was open and he went in. A brass plaque by the door read:

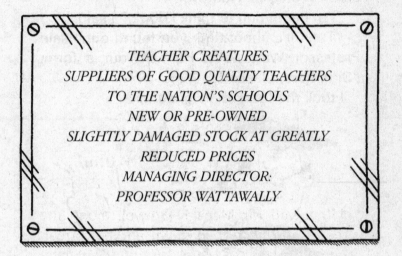

TEACHER CREATURES
SUPPLIERS OF GOOD QUALITY TEACHERS
TO THE NATION'S SCHOOLS
NEW OR PRE-OWNED
SLIGHTLY DAMAGED STOCK AT GREATLY
REDUCED PRICES
MANAGING DIRECTOR:
PROFESSOR WATTAWALLY

I followed Mr Meesley-Grewell in. No sooner was I in the hall, than I found myself facing a large man wearing a gown and a mortar board.

"My name's Professor Wattawally, can I help you?" asked the man.

"I'm looking for a teacher," I said.

"New or pre-owned?" Professor Wattawally asked.

"I don't know," I said.

"Bossy boots or dozy drawers?"

I shrugged. "Sorry. I don't understand what you're talking about."

"Don't you know anything about teachers?" asked Professor Wattawally.

"I'm beginning to think I don't," I said.

"Then it's about time you found out," said Professor Wattawally. He held out a form. "Sign here, please."

I took the form and signed...

"Right, Mr Here-Please," said Professor Wattawally. "You have just signed up to enrol on my special How To Handle Your Teacher course."

"How long is the course?" I asked.

"Oh, about 96 pages," said Professor Wattawally.

"That's all right then," I said. "Only I don't want to miss Chucklevision."

"Get along to your first lesson, then," said Professor Wattawally.

"Where do I go?" I asked.

"Just follow the arrows," explained Professor Wattawally.

So I did. And that is how I became an expert on how to handle teachers and was able to write this book...

How To Handle Your Teacher Key Stage 1

Understanding the basic fact: teachers aren't human

Now here's an interesting question: where do you come from? And I don't mean are you a Swede or a Turnip, or whether you come from Finland or Fatland or from Hungary or Thirstary, because that isn't a very interesting question at all.* I mean, how do you come to be on planet earth?

If you've done any PSHE at school, then of course the answer's easy-peasy. A kindly stork dropped you under a gooseberry bush and your mum came along and found you when she was picking gooseberries for a pie.

*Actually if you come from Thirstary, it is an interesting question, because I can't find Thirstary anywhere on my Pooh Bear Atlas of the World.

She was just about to put you in the saucepan with all the gooseberries when in the nick of time she said:

"Well bless my cotton drawers, this isn't a gooseberry, it's all purpley and shrivelled. It must be a prune."

She was just going to pour a jug of custard over your head, when you said "WAAAHHH!!!!"

And your mum said, "Well bless my cotton drawers, it's not a prune, either. It's a baby."

So you were brought up and taught how to clean your teeth, go to the toilet and brush your hair and then you were sent to school.

Now ask yourself this other interesting question: where do teachers come from? Were they dropped by storks under gooseberry bushes like the rest of us? Did they grow up to go to school like the rest of us?

The answer is – actually, I won't tell you the answer just in case there are teachers who have ignored the threat on the undercover overcover of this book and are reading this. Instead I will give you a clue, but one too tricky for any teacher to be able to work out. Here's the clue: the answer is a two letter word that begins with "n" and ends with "o".

It's obvious really. What kind of human being, if they'd been to school as a child, would then choose to spend the rest of their working lives in one? Put it another way: what kind of person in their right mind would choose to spend five days a week with the people in your class? OK, you may be an incredibly witty, intelligent and charming person – but what about some of your 29 classmates?*

*I'm thinking particularly of people like Billy Bonegrinder, Patti Poutalot, Salim Swearah, Ed Basher and Killer Sharkey.

Which means that your teacher must be either one or more of the following:

(TICK RELEVANT BOX)
LOOPY ☐
OUT OF THEIR TREE ☐
A FEW GHERKINS SHORT OF A BIG MAC ☐

A BLOOMING GREAT NORA ☐
NOT HUMAN AT ALL ☐

Now assuming you don't think your teachers are mad*, it stands to reason they can't be human at all.

Suddenly I jumped up in surprise. Then I jumped down again in surprise. Professor Wattawally was watching me.

"Has the penny dropped?" he asked.

"Not quite," I replied.

He let a coin fall from his hand. "It has now," he said.

"Yee-oww!" I said.

Because the penny had dropped. Right on my foot.

*They will be mad if they find you've ticked any of the five boxes. In fact, they'll not only be mad, they'll be livid, furious, raging, seething and wrathful as well. Not to mention just a teeny-weeny bit cross.

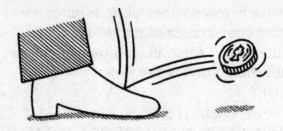

"Do you remember the brass plaque on my door?" asked Professor Wattawally.

I shook my head.

"Neither do I," said Professor Wattawally. "So let's go and see what it says again."

So we did.

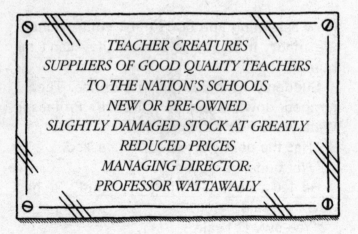

TEACHER CREATURES
SUPPLIERS OF GOOD QUALITY TEACHERS
TO THE NATION'S SCHOOLS
NEW OR PRE-OWNED
SLIGHTLY DAMAGED STOCK AT GREATLY
REDUCED PRICES
MANAGING DIRECTOR:
PROFESSOR WATTAWALLY

it said.

"Teacher Creatures is where I make the nation's teachers," Professor Wattawally went on.

"You mean sort of Roboteachers?" I asked.

"It's not so amazing," shrugged Professor Wattawally. "After all, you get Robocops and Robochefs, so why not Roboteachers?"

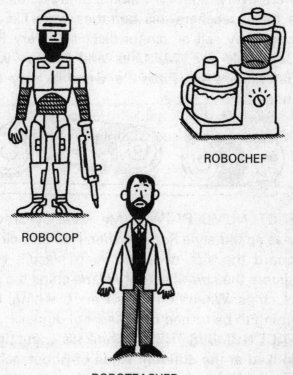

ROBOCHEF

ROBOCOP

ROBOTEACHER

A number of other facts fell into place. I made a sheet out of my duvet cover and then wrote all the facts down on it. In other words, this was my fact sheet:

FACT SHEET

FACT NUMBER ONE: Teacher Creatures was where my old teacher Mr Meesley-Grewell went every night for repairs. Being so old like a lot of teachers, his batteries were like the coke they sell at school discos (ie very flat). Being old too, his belts and pulleys were getting like his jokes (ie wearing very thin indeed).

FACT NUMBER TWO: Mr Meesley-Grewell was an old-style Roboteacher. He had a circuit board the size of a slimming biscuit, transistors the size of sausages and chips the size of chips. When he retires from teaching, he's going to be turned into a school dinner.

FACT NUMBER THREE: I think it's about time I looked at the different kinds of Roboteachers there are around and learnt how to handle them.

FACT NUMBER THREE AND A HALF: Wrong (wrote Professor Wattawally). It's about time for your Key Stage 1 SOOTS (SOME 'ORRIBLE OLD TEASERS) test.

1 How did your teacher arrive on planet earth?

a) Delivered by a stork.

b) Delivered by a rich, creamy, yellow dairy product that you spread on bread.

c) Built at Teacher Creatures.

2 Why shouldn't you let your teacher read this book?

a) Because it's too difficult for them to read.

b) Because they'd find it so interesting they wouldn't hear the bell and would stay in the staff room all day.

c) Because they'd find out how you are going to handle them before you do.

3 Which of the following things are characteristics of Roboteachers and which of Robochefs or Robocops?

(i) Can be described as:

a) A hard nut.

b) Good at chopping nuts.

c) Going nuts.

(ii) Enjoys:
   a) Beating villains up.
   b) Beating eggs for a delicious cake.

   c) Beating you to the front of the dinner queue.

(iii) Runs on:
   a) A futuristic, self-generating power source.
   b) Electricity.
   c) Can't run on and on without getting hopelessly out of breath.

ANSWERS:

1 a) Only people arrive this way. More concentration needed and less stork!
  b) Can't you tell stork from butter?
  c) Is ... the right answer! Take ten points!

2 a) Even if it is too difficult for them to read, they could still get someone else – like the school secretary – to read the long words for them, so watch it!
  b) This is a very good reason for letting them read this book.

c) Right. Take ten points. Unless you have let your teacher read this book, in which case they'll take all the points. Which is another good reason for not letting them read it!

3 (i) a) Robocops are this.
   b) Robochefs do this.
   c) Roboteachers are always doing this.

Take ten points for a right answer and fifteen points for a left answer.

3 (ii) a) What else does a Robocop do?
   b) Robochefs do this – but only when they're egged on.
   c) That's Roboteachers for you.

3 (iii) a) Robocops run on one of these.
   b) Most Robochefs use electricity.
   c) Roboteachers are always out of breath.

Take ten points for a right answer and take a drink for your teacher as well. They'll be thirsty after getting so out of breath.

WRITE YOUR TOTAL SCORE HERE:

HOW DID YOU SCORE?

110 points: OK smarty pants, do you want to write the rest of the book? Carry on, I don't care!

50–100 points: You're obviously trying. In fact, your teacher would probably say that you're very trying.

0–50 points: So, you think you're being taught either by an eight-foot giant clad in stainless steel armour or a food mixer. Better make an appointment with the optician.

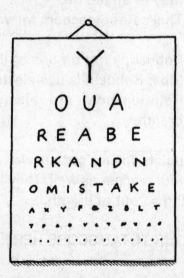

How To Handle Your Teacher Key Stage 2

Recognizing and handling the most common kinds of teachers

And so it was, the following Monday morning, that Professor Wattawally sent me out on teacher-handling practice, his words of advice implanted on my brain:

"The clues to all types of teachers are to be found in the weird and wonderful clothing that they wear, all of which are specially fitted to them at Teacher Creatures."*

*And if you don't believe teachers' clothes are weird and wonderful, just take a look at what your teachers are wearing.

I stood outside a school, the name of which was strangely familiar.

But this wasn't the school I was going to visit. It was not until about nine o'clock, that I found myself outside my destination.

"There you are!" I said to myself. "I've been looking for you everywhere!"

This was a school which was so hard and tough that even the teachers walked round in pears.

And very silly they looked, too. Then it hit me ...

... I told you it was tough. It was called Grunge Hall School. You might have seen it on the telly...

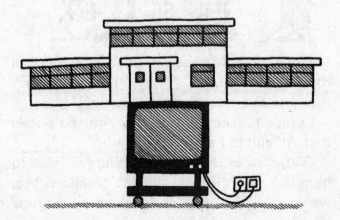

"Can you tell me where the Head Teacher is?" I asked a girl who had a ring in her ear. When I say she had a ring in her ear, I mean she was holding a mobile phone to it. She had some mates with her and they were listening to the latest Screaming Abdabs CD.

"He'll be under sedation in the medical room," said the girl. "They'll bring him back round at about four o'clock, though."

I gulped. "Under sedation? Are the pupils that difficult to handle?" I asked.

"Oh, it's not the pupils he finds difficult to handle," said the girl. "It's the teachers. Yes, we've got all types of teachers at Grunge Hall."

TEACHER-TYPE 1: BOSSY BOOTS

Suddenly, we heard a voice behind us. "Suzi Woozi!" it boomed sternly to the girl. "Get yourself into school. Don't you know the bell's gone?"

"Really?" said Suzi. "Has someone stolen it?"

"Are you taking the mickey?" said the voice, which belonged to a fierce-looking teacher.*

"No, sir," Suzi said. "I'm leaving it here."

"Get to your class," commanded the teacher. "Lessons started five seconds ago. And I'm putting your name in the late book."

"Yes, Dr Martens," said Suzi.

Dr Martens! Of course! The bootlaces as thick as liquorice sticks had been a clue, but now there was no doubt about it. With a name like Dr Martens, this had to be a BOSSY BOOTS teacher.

*I say the voice belonged to him, but like the bell, I suppose it might well have been stolen.

WARNING!!!
Not to be confused with GUM BOOTS
Teachers who are teachers who keep chewing
gum down their boots.

chew
chew

BOSSY BOOTS TEACHER   GUM BOOTS TEACHER

"Now where is the late book?" said Dr
Martens.

"Still in bed, I expect," said Suzi. "After all,
it is a late book! Ha! Ha!"

"You see what I mean about the teachers
being difficult to handle?" a sad-faced Suzi
said to me.

"Phoo-ey!" I replied. "I've been trained
in teacher handling skills by Professor
Wattawally!"

So I showed Suzi Woozi how to handle
BOSSY BOOTS teachers...

Handling a Bossy Boots Teacher – Method 1: Tie them up in knots

Because Bossy Boots teachers have most of their brains in their boots they easily get in a muddle. The next time Dr Martens found Suzi Woozi chatting and listening to CDs with her mates (ie eight seconds later) this is what happened...

DR MARTENS: What do you think you come to school for? To spend all morning chatting to your friends and listening to the latest Screaming Abdabs CD? Now get along to Miss Takes' room.*

SUZI: Yessir.

DR MARTENS: Make sure you apologize to her for your lateness.

SUZI: Yessir.

DR MARTENS: And see me at break.

*By which he meant Grunge Hall School's extremely large English teacher, more commonly known as "Big" Miss Takes.

SUZI: Yessir.

DR MARTENS: Well, what are you waiting for?

SUZI: Sorry sir, I'm trying to remember everything you said. What was the first thing?

DR MARTENS: (HE'S FORGOTTEN) Ummm...

SUZI: Something about "What do you think you come to school for to spend..."?

DR MARTENS: Oh yes! "... spend all morning chatting to your friends and listening to the latest Screaming Abdabs CD!"

SUZI: Can I really sir? Oh thank you very much sir!

RESULT: Suzi spent all morning chatting to her mates and listening to the latest Screaming Abdabs CD with Dr Martens' permission! Ye-e-eh!

Of course, there are other ways of tying a Bossy Boots teacher up in knots. Probably the most effective is to use their liquorice stick bootlaces. While they are bossing one of your mates, just tie them to each other – your teacher's laces that is, not your mate to your teacher. It's tricky, but have a go. If you can master this one, then you're a natural teacher handler and should go far. Unlike your teacher.

TEACHER-TYPE 2: CLEVER CLOGS

I left Suzi Woozi with her mates and went into school. Outside the first classroom a sad-faced boy in a Man United strip approached me.

"Are you a Teacher Handler?" he asked me.

"Yes," I replied. "How did you know? Are you psychic?"

"Wow! How did you know my name?" asked Si Kick.

"Because I'm psychic too," I replied.

"Can you help us with our teacher?" said Si Kick. He led me to the classroom door. The sign read:

> MISS KNOWALL

"Good morning, Miss Knowall," said Si, as he went in.

Ah, good morning, Si — said the teacher.

And bonjour, guten morgen,
buon giorno, kalimera,
how are you, watcha mate
and haway the lads!

Saying "good morning" in English wasn't good enough for Miss Knowall. She had to let you know that she knew how to say good morning in eight other different languages, including Cockney and Geordie. There was no doubt about it. Miss Knowall was a CLEVER CLOGS teacher.

WARNING!!!
Not to be confused with STUPID CLOGS teachers – Roboteachers built in the 1970s who, well … just wear stupid clogs (not to mention flared trousers, tartan hats and tank tops).

CLEVER CLOGS TEACHER STUPID CLOGS TEACHER

"Mental arithmetic," announced Miss Knowall to the class. "What's 2678 times 758? Without using your calculators! Si?"

"12 and a half?" Si suggested.

"No!" said Miss Knowall. "Goodness, it's really a very easy sum. I see you are going to have to do extra Maths homework. Now let's do some work on general knowledge. What's the name of the latest American space shuttle?"

"Red Dwarf?" suggested Si.

"Honestly," huffed Miss Knowall. "When I was your age I knew the name of every satellite, planet and constellation. Now, I think you'd all better read your Encyclopedias – all 56 volumes."

After the lesson I saw Si. "She really is appalling," he said.

I nodded.

"So how do we handle her?" asked Si.

I handed him a sheet of paper. "Everything you need to know is on here," I said.

Handling a Clever Clogs Teacher:
Ask a silly question

Ask any CLEVER CLOGS teacher the following questions and then watch them squirm as they try to work out the answer!

1 What's a frog's favourite drink?
Typical Clever Clogs Teacher Answer: Umm … stagnant pond water?
WRONG!!!
Right answer: Croaker Cola!

2 What do you call a dog with no legs?

Typical Clever Clogs Teacher Answer: Ummm … a noniped?
WRONG!!!
Right answer: Doesn't matter what you call him, 'cos he won't come anyway!

3 What's another name for the Four Tenors?
Typical Clever Clogs Teacher Answer: Ummm … Domingo, er … Pavarotti … er
WRONG!!!
Right answer: The Eight Fivers!

4 How do you make a Swiss cross?
Typical Clever Clogs Teacher Answer: Umm
... you draw a vertical line and an intersect-
ing horizontal line...
WRONG!!!
Right answer: You put ice cubes down the
back of his shirt!

5 What's the proper name for a man who
shears sheep?
Typical Clever Clogs Teacher Answer: Umm
... a sheep shearer?
WRONG!!!
Right answer: A Baaaaarber!

RESULT: Next lesson, I watched Miss Knowall
knitting her brows. Then at last she put her
needles down. "Ummm ... I don't think I do
know the answer to that one, Si," she said.
She spent the next hour with her head buried

in all 56 volumes of Encyclopedia Twitannica. She was concentrating so hard, she didn't see Si and his classmates slip copies of "Smash Hits" and "Shoot!" into their maths books. Ye-e-eh!

TEACHER TYPE 3: HOT SHOES

By now the word about me had spread all round the school.

"Excuse me," whispered a voice behind me. I turned round to find myself facing a lad who looked like your mum's conservatory after you've been playing football on the patio: ie completely shattered.

"My name's Harry Karry," said the lad. "Can you help me handle my teacher, Ms Wizbang?"

"Is something up with her?" I asked.

"Something's up, down, in, out and shake it all about with her," replied Harry Karry. "You have a look through our classroom window next lesson."

So I did.

"Right class," said Ms Wizbang, "this lesson we are going to be doing RE PE PSHE CDT and IT Ben get the pen Paul the ball Pia the gear four teams Fred you're Red Jasmeen Green Sue Blue Jack Black write on the computer about your teeth Keith the journey of the banana Rukshana underneath the story of the Ark Mark while you're running on the spot singing Lord of the Dance Lance yes Ness you too Hugh after three Lee..."

I was worn out just listening to Ms

Wizbang. There was no doubt about it, she was a typical HOT SHOES teacher. The sort who are so full of energy, their feet never touch the ground.

WARNING!!!
Not to be confused with SNOW SHOES teachers. These are PE teachers who play tennis standing on their hands.

HOT SHOES
TEACHER

SNOW SHOES
TEACHER

I slipped the following note into Harry Karry's hand while he was lying on the floor exhausted at the end of the lesson.

Handling a Hot Shoes Teacher:
Just weight and wait
This method will sort out your HOT SHOES teacher in eight easy steps (quick, quick, quick, quick, slow, quick, quick, quick). This method requires plaster of Paris. So this is what you must do:

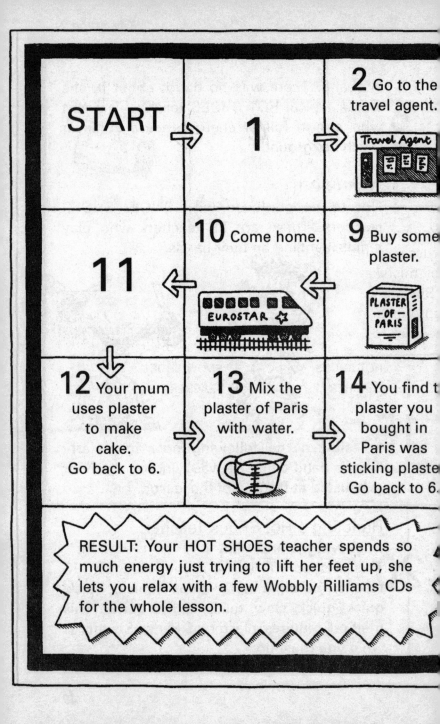

START → **1** → **2** Go to the travel agent.

10 Come home. ← **9** Buy some plaster.

11 ←

12 Your mum uses plaster to make cake. Go back to 6. → **13** Mix the plaster of Paris with water. → **14** You find the plaster you bought in Paris was sticking plaster. Go back to 6.

RESULT: Your HOT SHOES teacher spends so much energy just trying to lift her feet up, she lets you relax with a few Wobbly Rilliams CDs for the whole lesson.

TEACHER TYPE 4: DOZY DRAWERS

I was in the reception area looking at some pictures on the wall (obviously a class project on "Monsters from the X-files" I thought, until I saw the title "Teaching Staff; Grunge Hall School") when Wesley Presley called me into his classroom. "Can you help us with our teacher, please? Her name's Miss Gonallsoppy."

I looked at the teacher sitting in front of the class. There was a faraway look in her eyes. In fact, the look was so faraway I could hardly see it.

"We can't get her to take any notice of us at all," sighed Wesley Presley. "Listen to this."

I hid in the cupboard under the sink.

Wesley put his hand up. "Please Miss," he said. "Leonardo, the class hamster, has escaped from his cage and is about to jump down the back of your neck."

"That's very nice, dear," beamed Miss Gonallsoppy.

"And Miss," he continued, "Ali Pally's fallen off his chair and is writhing about on the floor being consumed by a fearsome godzilla-type monster, Miss."

"Just so long as he finishes his work," said Miss Gonallsoppy, dreamily.

"You see," said Wesley Presley. "She doesn't take any notice of us at all!"

"You should be grateful," I replied.

"You don't understand," said Wesley. "When we do have work, it's all soppy stuff. Like learning poems which go ...

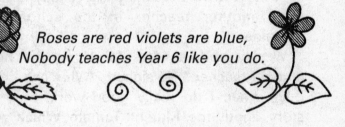

Roses are red violets are blue,
Nobody teaches Year 6 like you do.

and

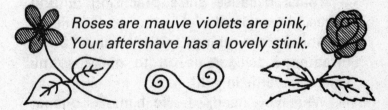

Roses are mauve violets are pink,
Your aftershave has a lovely stink.

"Ah," I said. "Your teacher is a classic example of a DOZY DRAWERS type teacher."

WARNING!!!
Not to be confused with CHEST OF DRAWERS teachers.

DOZY
DRAWERS
TEACHER

CHEST OF
DRAWERS
TEACHER

"Dozy Drawers teachers are usually in lurv with another teacher in the school," I explained.

Wesley nodded. "It's Mr Hunk, the new student teacher." He sighed. "What can I do? Even when I do really good work, like my story about the Mutant Tomato Which Ate Babies, she still puts lots of crosses on it."

"That's because she's practising writing kisses," I explained.

"And another thing," said Wesley. "She's threatened to get us all to make soppy Valentine cards in Art."

"What you need," I told him, "is one of these..."

Handling a Dozy Drawers Teacher: The all-purpose lurv-letter

Cross out any inappropriate words, sign with the name of the teacher your teacher is in lurv with and leave it on your teacher's desk:

Sweetikins*
My ~~darlingest~~ sweatikins**
Swotikins***

I think about you all the time. Your hair has the scent of flowers / cauliflowers. Your cheeks are like peaches / football peaches. Your eyes are like saucers / flying saucers. Your lips are like petals / bicycle petals.

Your ever loving honey pie

.........................(teacher's name)

*I know it's amazing, but this is how teachers who are in lurv talk to each other.
**I know it's amazing, but this is how PE teachers who are in lurv talk to each other.
***I know it's amazing, but this is how student teachers who are in lurv talk to each other.

RESULT: When Wesley Presley put a copy of this on Miss Gonallsoppy's desk, she was out of lurv with Mr Hunk before you could say "lovey-dovey". Wesley and his mates didn't have to make Valentine's cards in Art. In fact, they made paper whizzo-bombers, just like they always did in the good days before Miss Gonallsoppy was in lurv.

TEACHER TYPE 5: WOOLLY HAT

I sauntered out into the playground. A group of boys was playing football. They had already broken every downstairs classroom window. Now I knew why they called it break time.

I was hiding behind the dustbins making a few notes – mainly £20 and £50 ones – when Ali Pally came up to me.

"Can you tell me how to handle my teacher please?" he asked.

"What's wrong with her?" I replied.

"That's what's wrong with her," said Ali Pally. He pointed to the teacher on playground duty.

Even though it was a warm, sunny day, she was wearing a woolly hat. She was skipping around singing, "In and out the dusty bluebells; who will be my master." I couldn't imagine anyone being her master, not even the Demon Headmaster.

"Give us a break, Miss Craysey," said Ali.

CRASH! went another classroom window. It wasn't Miss Craysey giving him or anyone else a break, it was the lads playing football. Miss Craysey was too busy singing "In and out the dusty bluebells" to have noticed them.

"Your Miss Craysey is a classic example of a WOOLLY HAT Teacher," I said. "Or to put it more correctly, a Wally Hat Teacher."

WARNING!!!
Not to be confused with WELLY HAT teachers. These are simply teachers who like walking in the school pond – on their heads.

WALLY HAT
TEACHER

WELLY HAT
TEACHER

"Can she be cured?" asked Ali.
"If she's a side of bacon, she can," I replied.
"Help!" said Ali.

Miss Craysey was coming over. "Ali!" she called. "You can come and dance 'In and Out the Dusty Bluebells' with me."

"Sorry Miss, I've hurt my ankle," mumbled Ali.

"Nonsense!" yelled Miss Craysey as she hauled him off into the playground, where much to the merriment of all his friends, she whirled him in and out the dusty bluebells.

I observed proceedings from behind the dustbins. It was painful to watch. Mainly because the caretaker came out and threw 14 sacks of rubbish on my head.

Later on, in the medical bay, while I was having my head bandaged up and Ali was being treated for shock, I was able to go through with him the principal points of handling a Wally Hat teacher.

Handling a Woolly Hat Teacher: Act daft

The only way to handle a Woolly or Wally Hat teacher is to act as mad and daft as they are.

So when Ali was asked to dance with Miss Craysey, instead of saying he'd hurt his ankle, which was a very sensible answer, he should've said something completely daft, like "Sorry Miss, I'm allergic to gherkins." Leaving her too bewildered to make him do anything.

Here are some typical Wally Hat Teacher requests, with some pretty useless sensible replies and some really useful daft replies:

TYPICAL WALLY HAT TEACHER REQUESTS	SENSIBLE REPLIES	USEFUL DAFT REPLIES
Let's all pretend we're trees!	Can I do extra Maths instead?	Please Miss, I've just turned into a chain-saw.
	RESULT: You have to do extra Maths.	RESULT: You spend the lesson going Nee-ahhh!!

TYPICAL WALLY HAT TEACHER REQUESTS	SENSIBLE REPLIES	USEFUL DAFT REPLIES
Where's your homework?	Sorry Miss, I forgot it.	Please Miss, we've got an alien staying with us and he ate it.
	RESULT: Kept in at break.	RESULT: Your Woolly Hat Teacher gives you a packet of jammie dodgers for your alien's tea.
Who's going to help me make a giant pansy out of toilet roll holders?	I'm no good with my hands.	Excuse me Miss, the Draj of Zogma calls me from beyond the stars.
	RESULT: You get to be the giant pansy instead.	RESULT: You get the afternoon off as the inter-galactic space bus leaves at five past two.

TYPICAL WALLY HAT TEACHER REQUESTS	SENSIBLE REPLIES	USEFUL DAFT REPLIES
Where's your homework?	Sorry Miss, I forgot it.	Please Miss, it turned into a packet of cereal at breakfast.
	RESULT: Kept in at lunch time.	RESULT: You have to bring a packet of corn flakes into school each morning for the rest of the term.
Who'd like to sponsor me in the School Fête Goat Yoghurt Eating competition?	Sorry Miss, I haven't got any any money.	Sorry Miss, I'm a fruitarian.
	RESULT: You have to take part in the competition as well.	RESULT: Your teacher sends you home to get better.

TYPICAL WALLY HAT TEACHER REQUESTS	SENSIBLE REPLIES	USEFUL DAFT REPLIES
Where's your homework?	Sorry Miss, I forgot it. RESULT: Kept in at afternoon break	Please Miss, it spontaneously combusted on the way to school. RESULT: You're given the day off to go swimming to cool down.
We're all going to sing "Postman Pat" at class assembly.	Please Miss, I've got a sore throat. RESULT: You have to sing the part of Jess the cat.	Please Miss, I'll be time-travelling to the 22nd century tomorrow morning. RESULT: You're given the rest of the decade off school in order to complete your time travels.

Miaaaoowww!!

KEY STAGE 2: SOOTS TEST

Test your knowledge of different types of Roboteachers:

1 Match the following Roboteachers with the equipment needed to be able to handle them properly:

TYPE OF TEACHER	HANDLING EQUIPMENT NEEDED
a Woolly Hat	i Plaster of Paris
b Dozy Drawers	ii Liquorice stick boot-laces
c Bossy Boots	iii Lurv letter
d Clever Clogs	iv An exercise-book-eating alien
e Hot Shoes	v A frog, a Swiss and the Four Tenors

ANSWERS:
a=iv; b=iii; c=ii; d=v; e=i

SCORE: 10 points for each correct answer.

WHAT YOUR SCORE MEANS:

40-50 points: You've got the makings of a Clever Clogs teacher.

30-40 points: You've got the brains of an exercise-book-eating alien.

20-30 points: You've got the brains of a liquorice stick.

10-20 points: You've got the brains of a teacher.

0-10 points: You've got the brains of two teachers.

How To Handle Your Teacher Key Stage 3

Amazing! New! Improved!
Teachers and how to recognize
them

As you've probably realized, all the types of teachers we've looked at so far have been really old. However, the Teacher Creature factory has been busy developing amazing! new! improved! types of teacher, ready for the 21st century. It's easy to spot an amazing! new! improved! teacher. Having been made for the new millennium, they've all got millennium features:

NOT-VERY-AMAZING! OLD! IN-NEED-OF-IMPROVEMENT! TEACHER

AMAZING! NEW! IMPROVED! TEACHER

BALD DOME

MILLENNIUM DOME

I was invited take a look at some of these state-of-the-art teachers. Some had taken up posts in the country's toppermost schools:

Others had taken up posts in some of the country's bottommost schools:

This didn't please the Games teachers.

I had a choice of schools to visit. One was the country's top public school. I got there for lunch, but then I found it was Eton.

67

In the end I decided to visit a little place called Downwith School. Here I found three examples of the most modern and up-to-date teachers ever invented:

1: THE JOGGERAPHY TEACHER

No sooner had I walked through the school gates than I saw a crowd of children jogging round the playground each of them dressed in a different national costume. At their head was a teacher wearing not a whistle, but a compass round his neck. There was no doubt about it. This was the new model Roboteacher Mr Charles Atlas, a special money-saving combined PE and Geography Teacher, known as a Joggeraphy Teacher.

I left Mr Atlas just as he was about to kick off a game of football – using a globe instead of a ball, of course.

2: THE HOLOGRAM TEACHER

Next I walked straight through the school hall, straight through the adjoining classroom and straight through the teacher who was standing there.

"Aaaargh!!!!" I said. Then I said "Hello!"

"Hollo!" said the teacher.

"Yes, you are, aren't you," I replied. "Completely hollow."

"How could this be?" I asked myself.

"How should I know?" replied myself.

Then I saw the name plate on the teacher's classroom door:

MISS ELSE WARE

... it said. Amazing, I thought: a name plate that can talk!

It explained everything though. The reason the teacher was completely hollow and I had been able to walk right through her was obvious: she was elsewhere! In other words, she was  a Hologram teacher. She wasn't really there.* She was really in the staff room drinking mugs of coffee. It was just her hologram which I could see in the classroom.

Now, as you can imagine, just about every teacher in the world** wants to be a hologram, so they can sit in the staff room all day.

*Not to be confused with Miss Pratchett, who teaches recorder part-time. She's a teacher who isn't really *all* there. Not even on Monday and Wednesday afternoons when she is, if you see what I mean.

**Not to mention Mr Potts (also known as "Flower") who teaches Art and is out of this world.

It's also dead useful in lots of other ways.

For example, when you try the usual harm-less everyday tricks on your teacher, like putting a live frog in the register ...

... or putting a bucket of iced water above the door for when they come in ...

... or connecting the "Extra Homework" book to a two zillion volt electricity supply, it doesn't have any effect on them whatsoever.

If you want to check whether or not your teacher is a hologram, you can conduct this really simple experiment:

THE IS-MY-TEACHER-A-HOLOGRAM?-TEST

FIRST STEP: Walk through her. Or him. If you come out the other side, then your teacher is a hologram. If you fall flat on your bottom on the floor, your teacher is not a hologram.

In fact, they are more likely to be a HOLLERGRAM.*

3: THE HOLLERGRAM TEACHER

Creating a hologram teacher is, of course, a tricky business. Things do go wrong. So much so that I heard there were THREE mutant forms of Hologram teacher at Downwith School. And when I say heard, I mean heard...

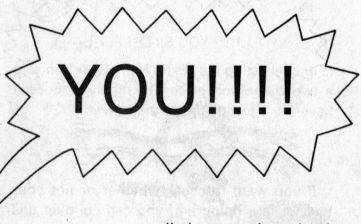

YOU!!!!

yelled a voice loud enough to have woken a hibernating warthog.

"Ah," I said. "Fancy bumping into you!"

Actually that wasn't exactly true, in fact it wasn't even inexactly true. I've never fancied bumping into any kind of teacher and this one was one of the least bumpable intoable

*I told you it was a really simple experiment: what I meant was it was an experiment only a really simple person would have bothered to try!

teachers I'd ever come across. The thing was, I'd bumped into this teacher, having mistaken him for a hologram. I knew he was a hollergram teacher and not a hologram teacher as soon as I heard him speak. Like all hollergram teachers he hollered with lots and lots of exclamation marks. He had black rimmed glasses a funny moustache and a cigar. There was no doubt about it, he was Mr Groucho Marx, one of the Exclamation Marx brothers.

YOU!!!!!! YOU SILLY PERSON!!!!

hollered Mr Marx. (Told you he was a groucho.)

ME:	(MEEKLY) Me sir?
MR MARX:	YES, YOU SIR!!!!! WHAT DID YOU WALK INTO ME LIKE THAT FOR?
ME:	Sorry sir.
MR MARX:	YOU COULD HAVE DONE SOME SERIOUS DAMAGE!!!* DIDN'T YOU SEE ME, OR WHAT?
ME:	Sorry sir. I thought you were a hooligan er ... I mean a hologram, sir.
MR MARX:	GRRR!!!
ME:	Have you got anything else to shout ... er, I mean say, sir, or shall I just crawl into this hole**?

4: THE HORROR-GRAM TEACHER

I was just having my lunch at Downwith School when I saw Mr Drack. I wished I hadn't. Mr Drack is a Horror-gram Teacher. Horror-gram teachers make the Demon Headmaster look like Mary Poppins. Mr Drack, the Horror-

*He's right. Hollergram teachers are usually so big that if they fall over they end up doing some serious damage ... like cracking the entire foundations of the school.
**The hole the hollergram teacher made when I knocked him over, that is.

74

gram teacher at Downwith School looked like this:

WARNING!!!
Readers of a nervous disposition, or even a nervous indisposition should skip over the next picture!*

I tried to get rid of Mr Drack by driving a steak through his heart. Unfortunately, the steak I was eating for my school lunch turned out to be a soya-bean rissole, so Mr Drack didn't wither away into a sticky mass of goo before my very eyes. In fact, the sticky mass of goo before my very eyes was my jam pudding and custard for afters.

*How to skip over the next picture: put the book on the floor, then take a rope and simply skip over it.

5: THE SUPER ROBOT TEACHER

Finally I came across a really super robot teacher at Downwith School and his name was Mr Triffick. Wow! Wicked! Brill! I can hear you thinking.*

You're imagining a super teacher, aren't you? The sort who gives you two-hour breaktimes, forgets about spulling tasts,** sets watching 20 episodes of Cartoon Capers as your homework and makes Barry Bludgeon*** stand upside-down with his face in the waste paper bin for two hours. Forget it – and I don't mean the spolling tusts. I mean Mr Triffick was a Super Robot Teacher. The sign on his door said:

NEW FROM TEACHER CREATURES
SUPER ROBOT TEACHER
MR TRIFFICK BA
LOTS OF MEGABYTES!!!
AMAZING RAM!!!

Yes, Mr Triffick was a Teacher With Improved Technology – or TWIT for short. His RAM was

*You really should get your brain oiled, you know.
**Dear Mr Writer, Do you mean spilling tosts? Kind Regards, The Publisher
***The class bully.

really amazing. Well, have you ever seen a pet sheep that can sing "The Wombles of Wimbledon"?

Mr Triffick did have lots of MEGABYTES, too. Unfortunately, these were on his leg where his amazing RAM had sunk his teeth into his shin. In many ways, Mr Triffick looked like his pet RAM, too. Hardly surprising really: he was a BA after all.

"Ah," said Mr Triffick, "I've forgotten your homework tonight which is to put Barry Bludgeon's head in the TV set. There are just two words for your spalling tist tomorrow. They are Cartoon and Capers."

I did say he was a TWIT. It looked as if this

teacher with improved technology could do with his technology being upgraded even further.

Just then Mr Drack came along. He had his eye on Mr Triffick's RAM. It looked at first as if he was for the chop. Then it looked at second as if he was the chop*.

I turned on my heel and ran out of Downwith School.

I turned the corner and ran out of breath.

Then I turned another corner and ran out of ... paper.

*The mutton chop Mr Drack was planning for his dinner, that is.

KEY STAGE 3: SOOTS TEST

1 What do you call a teacher who wears a compass instead of a whistle around their neck?

a) Lost.

b) A complete wazzock.

c) A Joggeraphy Teacher.

2 Which of the following three things is the most dangerous and terrifying to walk into?

a) A plate glass door.
b) A graveyard at midnight.
c) A Hologram Teacher.

3 Which of the following makes the most hideous racket?

a) The lead singer of the Screaming Abdabs.
b) A herd of elephants with stomach ache.
c) A Hollergram teacher.

4 Which of the following three hideous monsters is likely to give your nightmares?

a) A headless corpse.
b) Godzilla's granny.
c) A Horror-gram Teacher.

5 What do the letters TWIT stand for?

a) **T**eacher **W**ith **I**mpressive **T**attoo.
b) **T**eacher **W**ith **I**nk-stained **T**ie.
c) **T**eacher **W**ith **I**mproved **T**echnology.

ANSWERS:

1 a, b, c: all right! All right? 2a, 3a, 4a, 5a, all wrong. 2b or not 2b, 3b, 4b, 5b, all even wronger 2c, 3c, 4c, 5c, all correct!
SCORE: All right answers 1000 points. All wrong answers 1000th of a point.

6000–8000 points: Congratulations! You've reached Level 4. Now when you've finished, come back down again.
4000–6000 points: Pathetic! Now get down to the graveyard at midnight and see if you can answer the Spanish Inquisition's questions, you complete wazzock. And take Godzilla's granny with you!
0–4000 points: Appalling! Go back to school. Nursery school, that is. And take that Gestapo officer and that headless corpse with you, but don't let them frighten the little kiddies!

How To Handle Your Teacher Key Stage 4

Learning about just what goes on in the staff room

We all know what happens to teachers at break time and lunch time: they race off to the staff room and lock themselves in until the bell goes again. But what do they get up to when they're in there?

Let's open the staff room door at Grunge Hall School and have a look...

Of course! In their staff room, teachers do everything they've told you not to do in the classroom.

They put their feet up on the furniture.

prattle prattle

gossip gossip

They pick their noses.

They eat.

natter natter

drone drone

They sniff their armpits.

gab gab

chat chat

They ping bits of paper at Mr E B Jeebies.

burble burble

They talk. And talk. And talk. And talk.

Level of noise (in decibels)	STANDING UNDER A JET ENGINE	STANDING IN A HALL FULL OF SCREAMING ABDABS FANS	STANDING IN A SCHOOL STAFF ROOM

(Bar chart: Level of noise in decibels with values marked at 100, 200 and 1000. "STANDING UNDER A JET ENGINE" bar reaches about 100. "STANDING IN A HALL FULL OF SCREAMING ABDABS FANS" bar reaches about 200. "STANDING IN A SCHOOL STAFF ROOM" bar reaches above 1000.)

The next thing the teachers do is to all go "Ip Dip Sky Blue Who's It Not You". Then who-ever is "it", has to go out on playground duty. That's Miss Gonallsoppy.

Next, those who are left recharge their batteries. And I don't mean they plug them-selves into the light socket, though given the fact that teachers are robots, they might just as well.

Typical goings-on in a roboteacher's staff room

SMOKING
(What Roboteachers do when they've blown a fuse.)

TEACHERS' DIET:
High Optic fibre.
electrical juice.
micro chips.

Really ancient teachers who are steam powered run on coke and water.

How To Handle Your Teacher Key Stage 5

Learning about the power source

To really understand how Roboteachers work you have to understand their power source. This is the power source in a typical school:

HEAD TEACHER

Runs into his/her office.

DEPUTY HEAD TEACHER

Runs a shower (after taking Year 5 for PE).

SCHOOL SECRETARY
Runs the Head Teacher.

PARENT
Runs you to school and back in the car.

SCHOOL HAMSTER
Runs round and round getting nowhere.

SCHOOL GOVERNOR
Runs round and round getting nowhere.

THE SCHOOL CLEANERS

Run mops round the school. These people are so dangerous they're only allowed in after school's finished.

THE DINNER LADIES

Run the lunch box trollies over your feet. These formidable people used to serve Batman his lunch. ("Dinner, dinner, dinner, dinner Batman!!!" they used to sing.)

THE CARETAKER!!!

Runs the school.

SOOTS TEST 4: BUILDING YOUR OWN ROBOTEACHER

Can you build your very own Roboteacher, using the following items?

WOOLLY HAT

SCARY FACE
(Horror-gram teacher)

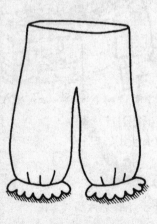

DOZY DRAWERS

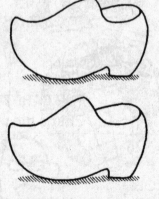

CLEVER GLOGS

SEE-THROUGH SHIRT
(Hologram teacher)

BOSSY BOOTS

HOT SHOES

GLOBE
(Joggeraphy teacher's
football)

MEGAPHONE
(Hollergram
teacher)

SOOTS TEST 5: BUILDING YOUR OWN IDEAL TEACHER

Can you build your own ideal teacher, using the following items?

ROSE TINTED GLASSES
They'll never believe it was you who put shoe polish in the soap dispenser in the staff toilet.

MAKE UP
To allow you to make up any excuse about anything.

PULLOVER
For pulling the wool over her eyes.

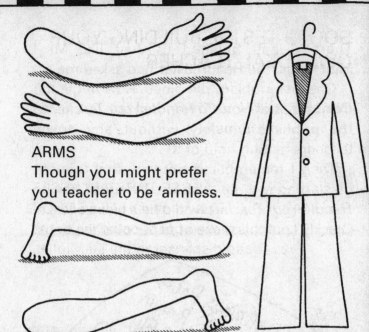

ARMS
Though you might prefer
you teacher to be 'armless.

LEGS
Though after the staff
Christmas party your
teacher might be legless.

CASUAL SUIT
A casual attitude
to your work
(or lack of it)
will suit you.

PER-SUEDE SHOES
To make it easy for you
to persuade her to do
what you want.

There! I had finished it! Just like Mr I Mincharge, the Headmaster had asked me to.

One last problem remained. How to get the manuscript of *How To Handle Your Teacher* to the publishers safely without any nosey teachers getting hold of it!

Then I remembered my very first thought on starting to write the book. I thought *How to Handle Your Teacher* would be a piece of cake. Quickly I put this piece of paper over the book:

Now *How To Handle Your Teacher* really was a piece of cake.

"Ah ha," said a voice behind me. It was Dr Martens, the Bossy Boots teacher. "What are we trying to hide in there?"

"Nothing," I said.

"Nothing?" said Dr Martens. "That doesn't look like nothing. What is it? Let's have the truth. I wasn't born yesterday. What do you think I am?"

"A fruit-cake, sir," I said.

Dr Martens was beginning to look like a sauna, in other words very steamed up. I raced out of Downwith School and ran all the way to my publisher's offices in Deadline Lane.

And the rest, as they say, is History.

Not to mention Geography, English, Maths, Science, PHSE, Art, Music, PE, Games...

How To Handle Your Teacher Key Stage 6

Create your teacher register

YOUR NAME			
SCHOOL			
CLASS GERBIL'S NAME			
SCHOOL GOLDFISH'S NAME			
TEACHER'S NAME	TEACHER'S NICKNAME	TYPE	SUCCESS-FULLY HANDLED (DATE)

YOUR HOW TO HANDLE YOUR TEACHER SOOTS TEST RESULTS:

Add up your total points for each test here:

	MY POINTS	TOTAL POSSIBLE POINTS
TEST 1		110
TEST 2		50
TEST 3		8000
TOTAL		8160

HOW DID YOU SCORE?

More than 8159 points: You must have a super brain in your head.

Less then 8159 points: You must have a brain of soup in your head.

How To Handle

If you think you've mastered how to handle your teacher, let's see if you can get one over on some of these people:

How to Handle Your Mum

How to Handle Your Dad

How to Handle Your Gran

How to Handle Your Brother/Sister

Our step-by-step guides help you keep *everyone* in line!